The
HANDY
GADGET Catalogue

Handy Gadgets for REALLY Old People!

Written and Illustrated by Sophia J. Ferguson

www.grandpamudcake.com

First published in Great Britain 2022 by Macnaughtan Books
Text and illustration copyright © Sophia J. Ferguson

ISBN: 978-1-8383617-1-6

CONTENTS ✳

1. The HANDS-FREE BOOK HAT

Reading a book and having a snack at
the same time can be **VERY** tricky indeed...

...but **NOT** with the Hands-Free Book Hat!

Put the hat on, attach your favourite book, and
BOTH your hands are free for a drink and a snack!

Available in three **FASHIONABLE** hat styles...

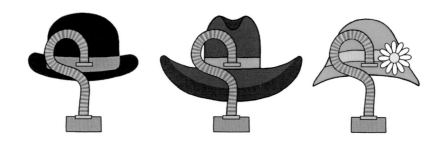

WARNING
The Hands-Free Book Hat must be used
while sitting down ONLY!

2. The CHATTY ROBOT VACUUM

Vacuuming your home can be
EXHAUSTING...

That's why you need **GORDON**, the Chatty
Robot Vacuum, to do the hard work for you!

Gordon will keep your floors **SPARKLING** clean
AND he'll chat to you while he works.

If you **HATE** cleaning and you like to chat, you will **LOVE** Gordon, the Chatty Robot Vacuum!

RELAX in your armchair while Gordon chats and cleans.

3. The **ANTI-DRIBBLE TV DINNER TRAY**

It's fun to have dinner in front of
the TV, but it's NO fun when you
DRIBBLE food down your front.

It's time for the
Anti-Dribble TV Dinner Tray!

Simply hang the TV Dinner Tray over
your shoulders and eat dinner
WITHOUT ruining your jumper!

Say goodbye to TV dribbles **FOREVER**

4. The HEATED PURRING CAT

Are you a cat lover who doesn't want to live with a **REAL** cat?

Meet Matilda, the **ADORABLE** Heated Purring Cat!

When you switch Matilda on, she warms up and starts to **PURR** - just like a real cat!

Matilda will keep you warm
ALL winter!

She's the **EASIEST** pet ever.
No need to buy cat food!

5. The ITCHY BACK SCRATCHING GRABBER

Do you sometimes have an **ITCHY** back which you can't quite scratch?

Is it hard for you to **BEND OVER** to pick something up?

The Itchy Back Scratching Grabber will do **BOTH** of these jobs for you!

6. The TALKING WALKING STICK

Do you sometimes get **LOST** when you go out for a walk?

The Talking Walking Stick will help you find your way home...

Switch it on and it will tell you **EXACTLY** where you need to go.

7. The ADULT SNOOZE BUGGY

Do you sometimes feel **SLEEPY** when you're out shopping?

Take the Adult Snooze Buggy with you and have a quick **SNOOZE** whenever you need one!

Buggies aren't just for **BABIES!**

The Snooze Buggy folds up EASILY
after you've had your nap.

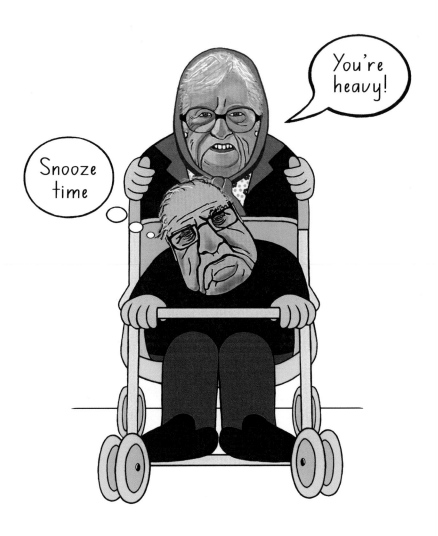

Large adults my be difficult to push!

8. The HANDY CAR PARKING FLAG

Do you sometimes **FORGET** where
you parked your car?

Attach the Handy Car Parking Flag
to your car and you'll be able
to spot it **MILES** away!

Available in **FOUR** easy-to-spot colours.

NEVER lose your car again!

9. The LOOKALIKE GARDEN GNOME

Do you ever dream of having a **GARDEN GNOME** that looks like you?

Send in your photograph and we'll make a garden gnome that looks **EXACTLY** like you!

Put it in your front garden and your
neighbours will be **AMAZED!**

Order your gnome **TODAY!**

10. The NANTENDO GAME GIRL

Are you a Grandma who likes **GAMING?**

Give your brain a workout with the **INCREDIBLE** Nantendo Game Girl!

It comes with a selection of **EXCITING** games **JUST** for Grandmas, including...

Gaming's **NOT** just for kids!

COMING SOON
The Grandtendo Game Boy
for Grandpas!

11. The ELECTRIC BOBBLE HAT

Keep your head **COSEY** with the
Electric Bobble Hat!

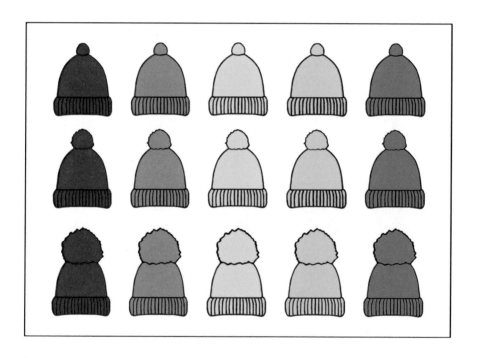

Available in three **BOBBLE** sizes –
SMALL, MEDIUM and LARGE – and five
AMAZING colours!

Which one will you choose?

Charge up your Electric Bobble Hat
before you go out...

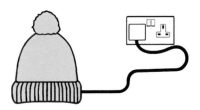

...and your head will stay warm **ALL** day long.

IDEAL for Grandpas who don't
have much hair!

12. The DANCING-SINGING POT PLANT

Do you wish your pot plants
were a bit more **EXCITING?**

Stand next to the Dancing-Singing
Pot Plant and it will sing you
a **WONDERFUL** song!

It doesn't just sing -
it **DANCES** too!

One hundred **FABULOUS** songs
to sing and dance along to!

13. The RUBBER BUBBLE DUCK

Do you enjoy a rubber duck at bathtime?
Do you like a bath **FULL** of bubbles?

If you do, you will **LOVE**
the Rubber Bubble Duck!

Switch it on and watch it blow **BEAUTIFUL**
bubbles while you soak in the tub.

Order the **REMARKABLE**
Rubber Bubble Duck today!

It's **REMARK-A-BUBBLE!**

14. The GIANT FUR BOOT

Do your feet feel **FREEZING**
cold in winter?

The **LUXURIOUS** Giant Fur Boot
is exactly what you need!

Take off your socks and slip your feet into
the **HEAVENLY** fur lining.

Keep your toes **TOASTY** in winter.

WARNING
Do NOT attempt to walk while wearing
the Giant Fur Boot!

15. The **4-SPEED ELECTRIC ROCKING CHAIR**

Do you run out of energy when
you rock your rocking chair?

The **INCREDIBLE** 4-Speed Electric
Rocking Chair will do the rocking for you!

Simply plug it in and choose your favourite
rocking speed on the handy remote control.

☀ Which Handy Gadget Will You Order? ☀

1. The **HANDS-FREE BOOK HAT**

2. The **CHATTY** ROBOT VACUUM

3. The **ANTI-DRIBBLE** TV DINNER TRAY ☀

4. The **HEATED** PURRING CAT ☀

5. The **ITCHY BACK** SCRATCHING GRABBER ☀

6. The **TALKING** WALKING STICK ☀

7. The ADULT SNOOZE **BUGGY** ☀

8. The **HANDY CAR** PARKING FLAG ☀

9. The **LOOKALIKE** GARDEN GNOME ☀

10. The **NANTENDO** GAME GIRL ☀

11. The **ELECTRIC** BOBBLE HAT ☀

12. The DANCING-SINGING **POT PLANT** ☀

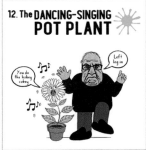

13. The **RUBBER** BUBBLE DUCK ☀

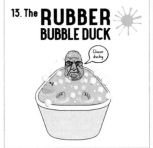

14. The **GIANT** FUR BOOT ☀

15. The **4-SPEED ELECTRIC** ROCKING CHAIR ☀

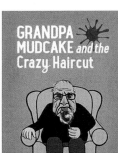

GRANDPA MUDCAKE *and the* **Crazy Haircut**

by Sophia J. Ferguson

GRANDPA MUDCAKE *and the* **Crazy Tea Party**

by Sophia J. Ferguson

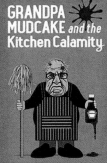

GRANDPA MUDCAKE *and the* **Kitchen Calamity**

by Sophia J. Ferguson

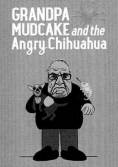

GRANDPA MUDCAKE *and the* **Angry Chihuahua**

by Sophia J. Ferguson

GRANDPA MUDCAKE *goes* **Internet Shopping**

by Sophia J. Ferguson

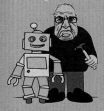

GRANDPA MUDCAKE *and the* **Rickety Robot**

by Sophia J. Ferguson

GRANDPA MUDCAKE *and the* **Nosey Chicken**

by Sophia J. Ferguson

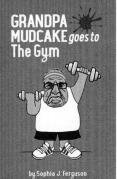

GRANDPA MUDCAKE *goes to* **The Gym**

by Sophia J. Ferguson

The **HANDY GADGET** *Catalogue*

A Grandpa Mudcake SPECIAL EDITION
by Sophia J. Ferguson

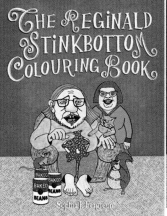

THE REGINALD STINKBOTTOM COLOURING BOOK

Sophia J. Ferguson

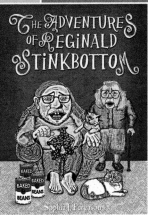

THE ADVENTURES OF REGINALD STINKBOTTOM

Sophia J. Ferguson

GRANDPA MUDCAKE.com

Made in United States
North Haven, CT
29 November 2022

27504902R00022